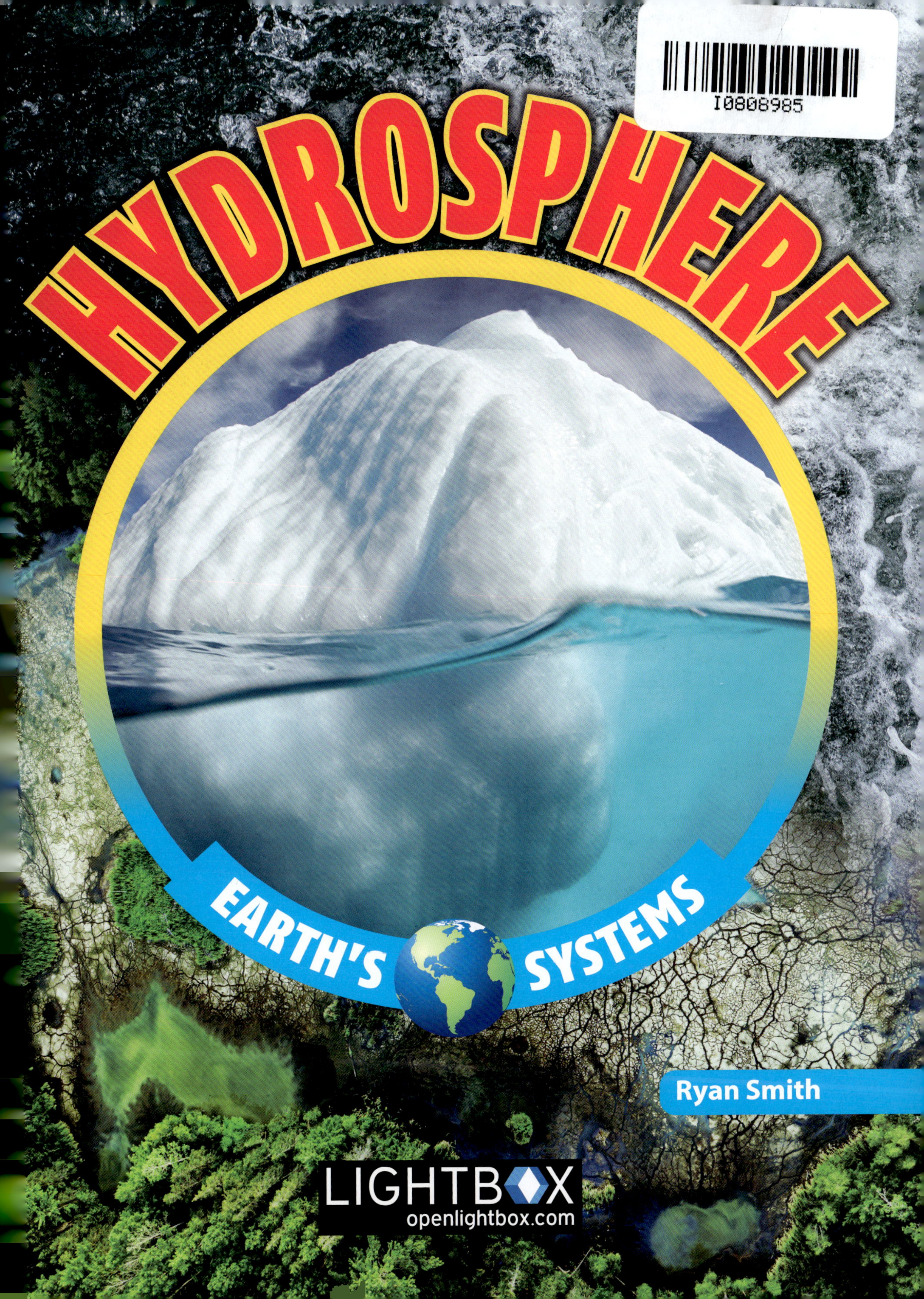

HYDROSPHERE
EARTH'S SYSTEMS
Ryan Smith
LIGHTBOX
openlightbox.com

Go to
www.openlightbox.com
and enter this book's unique code.

ACCESS CODE

LBXD8726

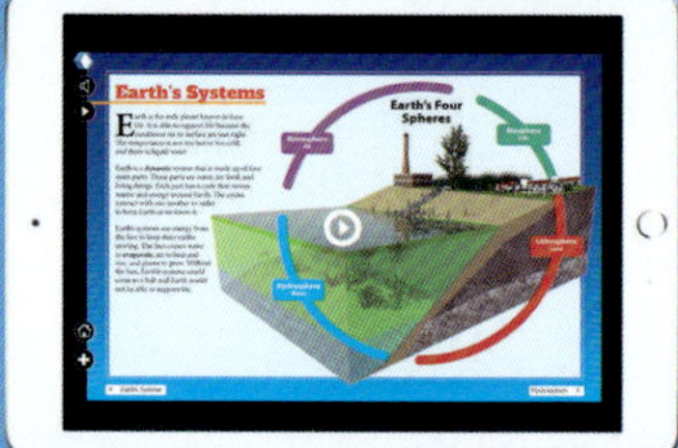

Lightbox is an all-inclusive digital solution for the teaching and learning of curriculum topics in an original, groundbreaking way. Lightbox is based on National Curriculum Standards.

LIGHTBOX SUPPLEMENTARY RESOURCES

SHARE
Share titles within your Learning Management System (LMS) or Library Circulation System

CURRICULUM
Find national and state curriculum correlations

CITATION
Create bibliographical references following the Chicago Manual of Style

STANDARD FEATURES OF LIGHTBOX

AUDIO High-quality narration using text-to-speech system

ACTIVITIES Printable PDFs that can be emailed and graded

SLIDESHOWS Pictorial overviews of key concepts

VIDEOS Embedded high-definition video clips

WEBLINKS Curated links to external, child-safe resources

TRANSPARENCIES Step-by-step layering of maps, diagrams, charts, and timelines

INTERACTIVE MAPS Interactive maps and aerial satellite imagery

QUIZZES Ten multiple-choice questions that are automatically graded and emailed for teacher assessment

KEY WORDS Matching key concepts to their definitions

Lightbox Grades 3–5 Subscription
ISBN 978-1-5105-5424-5

Access hundreds of Lightbox titles with our digital subscription. Sign up for a **FREE** subscription trial at **www.openlightbox.com/trial**

HYDROSPHERE

CONTENTS

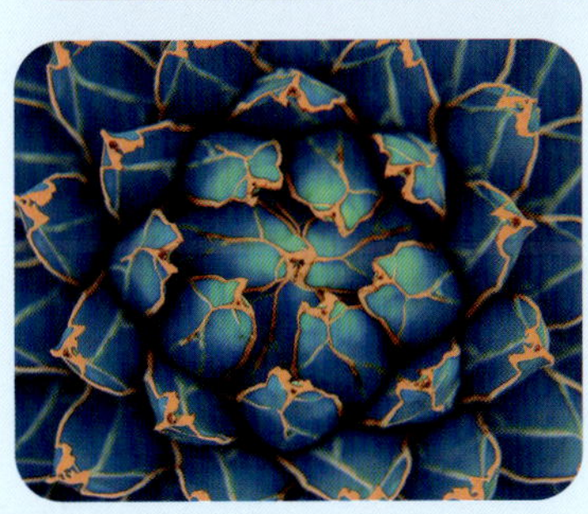

Earth's Systems

Earth is the only planet known to have life. It is able to support this life because the conditions on its surface are just right. The temperature is not too hot or too cold, and there is liquid water.

Earth is a **dynamic** system that is made up of four main parts, or "spheres." These parts are water, air, land, and living things. Each part has a cycle that moves matter and energy around Earth. The cycles interact with each other in order to form Earth as we know it.

Earth's systems use energy from the Sun to keep their cycles moving. The Sun causes water to **evaporate**, air to heat and rise, and plants to grow. Without the Sun, Earth's systems would come to a halt and the planet would not be able to support life.

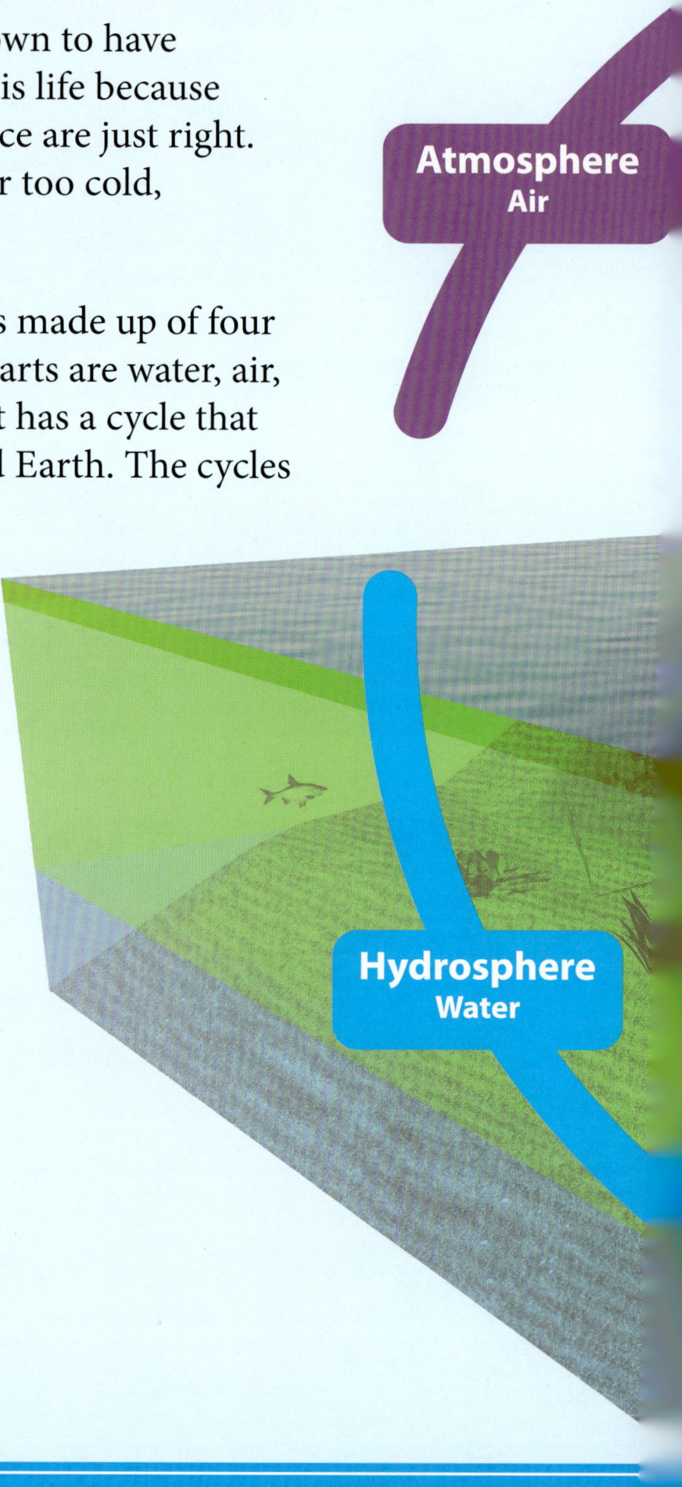

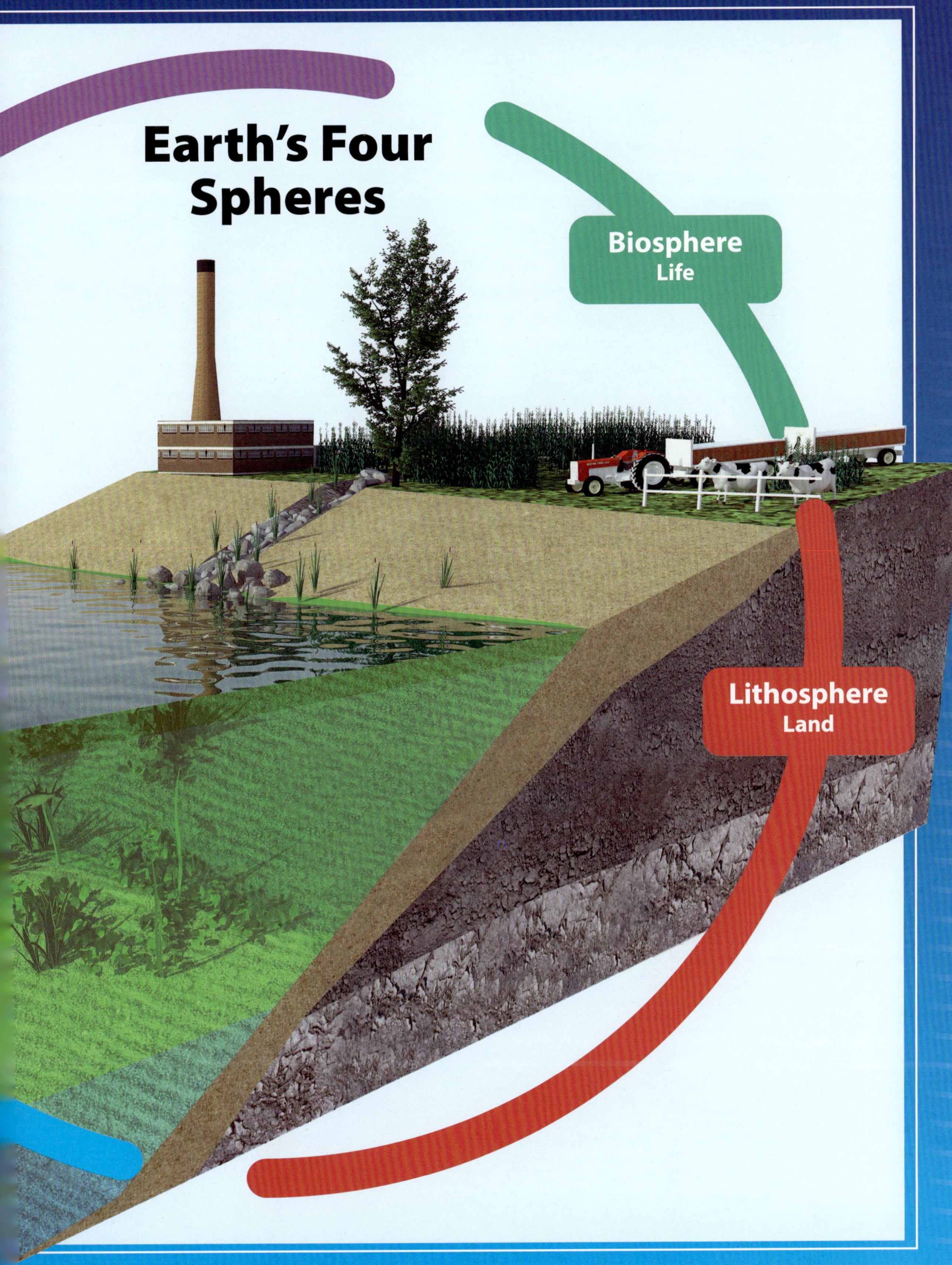
Earth's Four Spheres
Biosphere
Life
Lithosphere
Land

The Pacific Ocean is the largest water mass on Earth. It covers more than 30 percent of the planet's surface.

The Hydrosphere

The hydrosphere consists of all the water on, over, and under Earth's surface. Most of the water on Earth is in the ocean. While the ocean is technically one body of water, it is divided into five regions. These are the Atlantic Ocean, Pacific Ocean, Indian Ocean, Arctic Ocean, and Southern Ocean.

More than 70 percent of Earth's surface is covered by liquid water. Water can also be found in the air as water vapor and clouds, as well as frozen in ice caps and **glaciers**. Liquid water exists as either salt water or fresh water. Salt water is found in seas, oceans, and certain lakes.

Fresh water can be found trapped in ice, traveling down rivers, collecting in lakes, or in the ground. Most of the fresh water stored in glaciers and ice caps remains frozen all year, making it difficult for people to access. Rivers contain much less water than glaciers and ice caps, but the water in them is accessible. A large portion of the water people and animals use comes from rivers.

Rivers flow downhill. They often empty into the ocean, but may also flow into aquifers or lakes. Aquifers are underground rock layers that collect and trap groundwater. Lakes are large, landlocked bodies of water. They are filled by rivers or springs and drain into rivers or aquifers.

Distribution of Earth's Water

The vast majority of Earth's water is salt water, which is not safe for humans to drink. Only a small fraction of water is accessible surface fresh water. This water is often found in lakes, rivers, and wetlands. It is what people usually drink and use for other purposes.

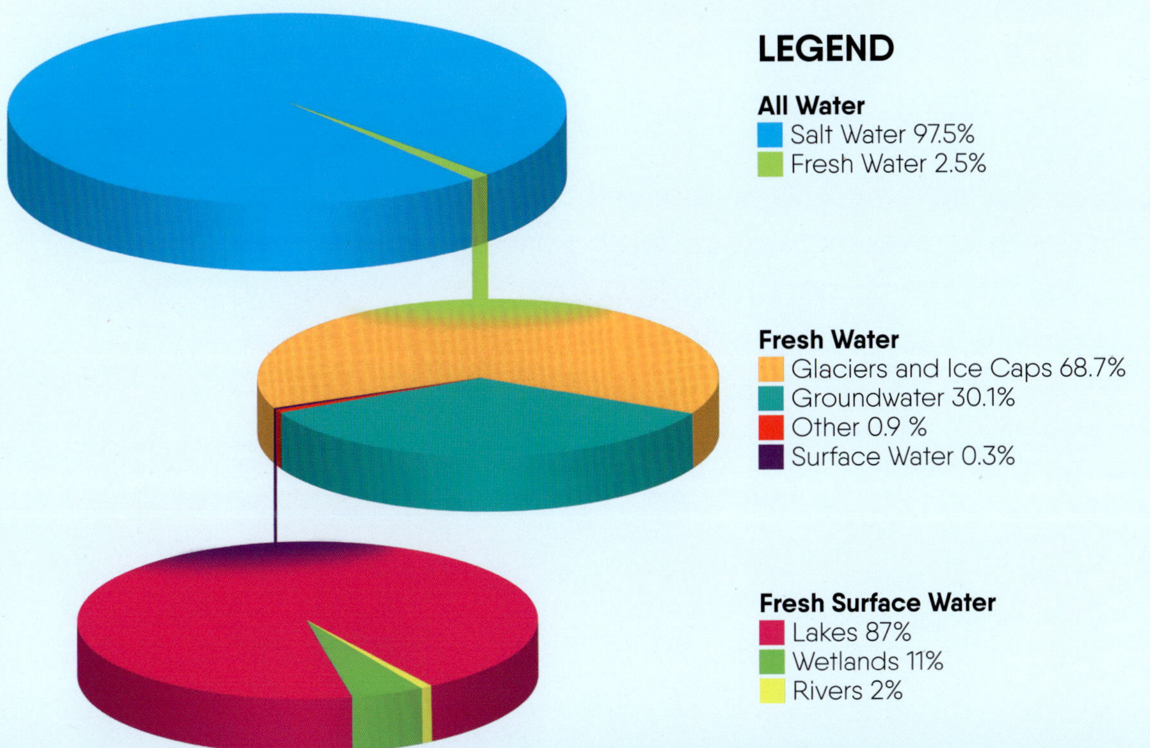

The Water Cycle

The natural movement of water through the hydrosphere is called the water cycle. It involves water changing in state from solid to liquid to gas and back again as it moves. In its simplest form, the water cycle involves heat from the Sun causing glaciers to melt. The runoff from glaciers eventually collects and forms rivers, which make their way to the ocean.

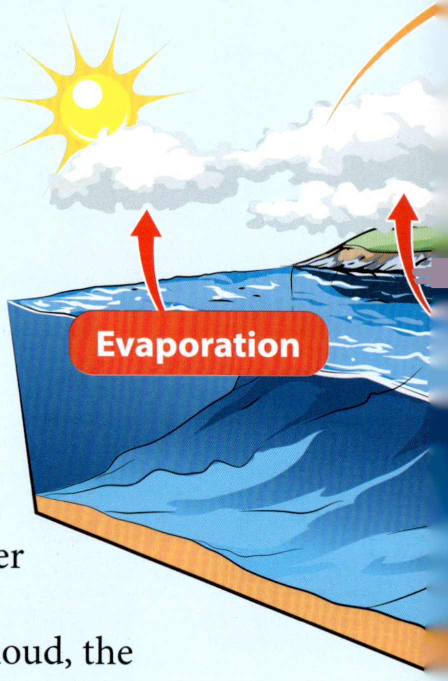

Evaporation

Once water reaches the ocean, it has nowhere else to flow. However, heat from the Sun causes the ocean water to evaporate and turn into water vapor. This vapor then cools and **condenses** to form clouds. Once there is enough water in a cloud, the water falls as rain or snow. **Precipitation** collects in lakes, rivers, aquifers, and glaciers, and the cycle begins again.

Water does not have to go through every step in this cycle. It may evaporate from lakes or rivers instead of reaching the ocean, or it may become trapped in aquifers or glaciers and stop moving through the cycle until it is released. Water can also remain in lakes and oceans for a long time before it evaporates.

States of Matter

Water can exist as a solid, liquid, or gas. These are the three states of matter. Water changes from one state to another as it heats or cools.

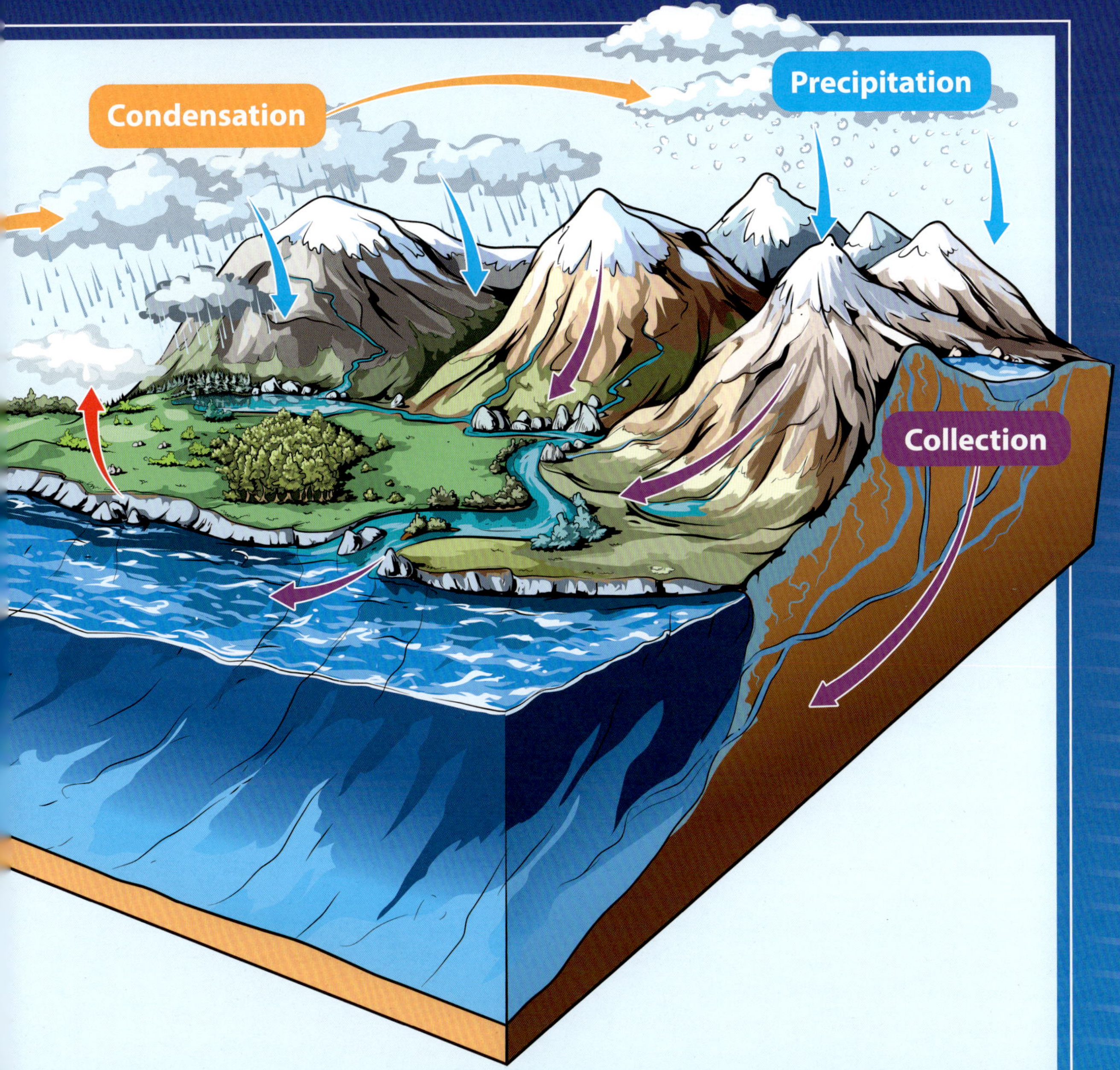
Condensation
Precipitation
Collection

Ice
Melting
Freezing
Liquid Water
Evaporation
Condensation
Water Vapor

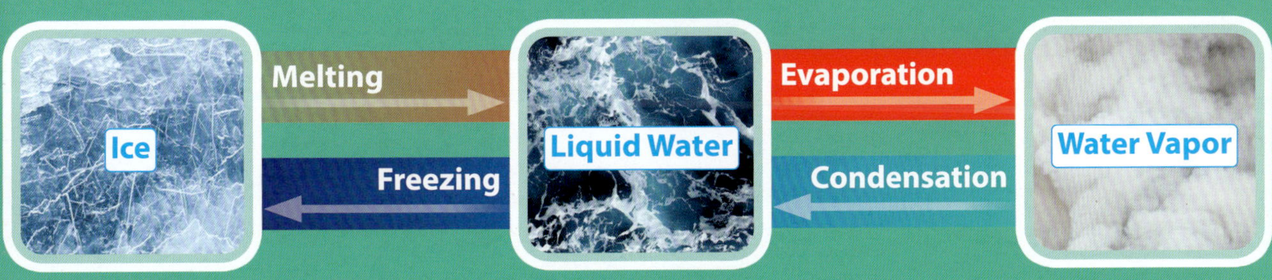

Around the World

The hydrosphere is a large and complicated system that covers the entire world. Some parts of the world have high rates of evaporation and very little precipitation. Other areas have an abundance of lakes and rivers and experience frequent rainfall.

1 Hubbard Glacier, North America

Alaska's Hubbard Glacier is a tidewater glacier. This means that it extends right into the ocean. Chunks of the glacier break off and form icebergs. Hubbard is the largest tidewater glacier in North America. It is also one of the few glaciers in the world that is still growing despite an increase in global temperatures.

2 Sahara Desert, Africa

The Sahara Desert only has two rivers, the Nile and the Niger, running through it. Parts of the Sahara can go years without getting any rain. However, large amounts of water can be found in the aquifers beneath the desert. At the lowest points in the desert, these aquifers feed small aboveground pools called oases.

3 Sundarbans Mangrove Forest, Asia

The Sundarbans **mangrove forest** is one of the largest mangrove forests in the world. It covers nearly 4,000 square miles (10,000 square kilometers) of coastal land. The forest is a World Heritage site. It is home to many **halophytic** plants and endangered species, such as the Bengal tiger.

Many desert communities have developed around oases.

Living with the Hydrosphere

People need water in order to survive. Communities have to find ways to both use and coexist with the hydrosphere. Too much water can make survival almost as difficult as too little water.

Desert communities do not often have access to surface water bodies such as lakes or rivers. Instead, they tend to get their water from aquifers. Rainwater seeps through the ground and collects in the aquifers. Water from aquifers may find its way to the surface through natural springs or be pumped to the surface by people. Desert communities have to be careful not to pump all of the water out of their aquifers.

In many countries, machines called snowplows are used to clear heavy snow from roads.

Other communities have to prevent large amounts of precipitation from impacting everyday life. In Alaska, some areas can receive an average of 60 inches (152 centimeters) of snow in a year. Communities that experience heavy snowfall must find ways to clear the snow from roads, parking lots, and sidewalks so that people are able to continue with their usual activities.

Pang uks

The fishing village of Tai O in Hong Kong is famous for its stilt houses, called Pang uks. Fishers built their houses on stilts in order to keep them from being washed away by **typhoons**. With their boats tethered at their doorstep, fishers have easy access to the waters in which they fish.

Human Activity

The hydrosphere plays an important role in the work people do. From fishing to shipping to watering crops, people constantly interact with the hydrosphere in order to make a living. Human activity depends heavily on oceans, rivers, and lakes.

Fishing boats can be found in every ocean on Earth.

Commercial fishing takes place in both fresh water and salt water. About 250 million people work in the fishing industry. Fishers use nets to harvest fish such as cod, haddock, herring, and tuna. Traps are used to catch crabs, lobsters, and other crustaceans. Fishing is one of the oldest ways of gathering food. Archaeological evidence shows that ancient humans caught fish and collected mollusks.

The shipment of goods around the world by freighters is another way people rely on the hydrosphere for work. Ocean freight is one of the most cost-effective ways to ship large amounts of goods around the world. It is also the most cost-effective way to ship heavy items such as cars. More than 10 billion tons (9 billion metric tons) of goods were shipped across the ocean in 2018.

Some freighters can carry about 8,000 cars at a time.

Many farmers set up sprinklers to automatically spray crops at set times.

Farming is an industry that would not be possible without the hydrosphere. Farmers need large amounts of water to grow their crops. In the past, they had to rely on rain to provide this water. Today, many farms have irrigation systems that collect water and apply it to crops regularly. Modern irrigation systems help farmers find ways to make sure the water is used by the crops and not evaporated by the Sun.

Human Impact

The human impact on the hydrosphere is the result of how closely people interact with water bodies in order to live and work. Human actions have both direct and indirect effects on the hydrosphere.

Scientists regularly test the water quality of rivers and lakes.

One of the most significant ways that humans have impacted the hydrosphere is through pollution. Garbage, sewage, and chemicals are often dumped into water bodies or find their way into the hydrosphere through runoff. These pollutants make rivers and lakes unsafe to use for drinking water. They can also have harmful effects on aquatic plants and animals.

Pollutants in the air can find their way into the hydrosphere, too. Gases released from the production of goods and the burning of **fossil fuels** may make precipitation more acidic. This polluted rain, known as acid rain, adds pollutants to lakes, rivers, and soil. Acid rain may also speed up the **erosion** of certain rocks and minerals.

The gases that cause acid rain are mostly produced by factories and power plants.

Greenhouse Gases

Some of the pollutants in the air are considered greenhouse gases. They trap heat in the same way a greenhouse does. An increase in global temperatures, caused by greenhouse gases, is one of the main reasons that the world's glaciers are melting at alarming rates. Should glaciers disappear altogether, many places would run out of water. Other places along coastlines would no longer be livable due to rising oceans caused by glacial runoff.

Some large plants in coastal areas use reverse osmosis to remove salt from sea water.

Science and Progress

Water shortages exist around the world. Many people do not have access to enough clean fresh water. In response to the growing demand for clean water, scientists are finding new ways to harness, clean, and use water. These innovations aim to help make sure people have access to clean water both now and in the future.

For communities that live near the ocean, having a way to turn salt water into fresh water would help solve water shortages. That is why scientists are working to make **desalination** an affordable process. Traditional desalination processes involve boiling salt water in order to separate out the salt. This requires a large amount of energy and is not very efficient. Newer technologies are using a method called reverse osmosis. Scientists are looking for ways to filter salt water that require even less energy than the reverse osmosis method.

Reverse Osmosis

Reverse osmosis involves pushing salt water through a series of filters in order to remove the salt.

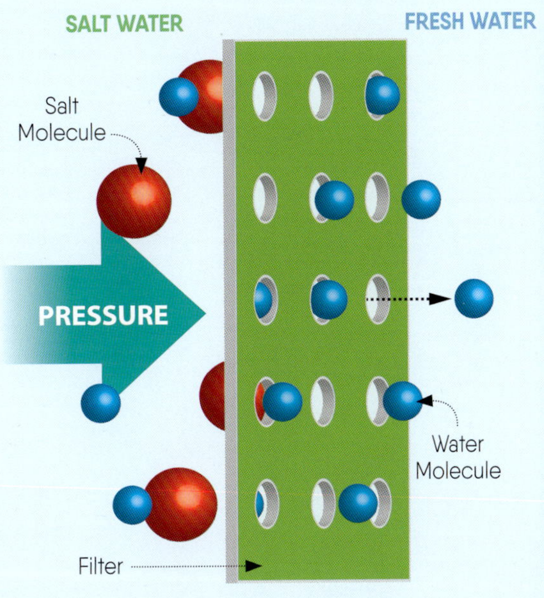

Communities are also finding creative ways to collect water. In some places that experience large amounts of fog, people have set up mesh nets on hillsides. The water vapor in the fog condenses when it comes in contact with the nets, forming water droplets. These droplets run down the nets and are collected in containers.

Weather conditions determine how much water a fog net collects in a day.

The Hydrosphere through Time

6 MILLION BC

The Colorado River begins to erode the Colorado Plateau. This river will eventually form the Grand Canyon.

18,000 BC

The size of the ice sheets covering North America peaks. Approximately 32 percent of Earth is covered by glaciers.

6000 BC

Irrigation is practiced in Egypt. Floodwaters from the Nile River are diverted to farmers' fields in order to water crops.

The hydrosphere has played an important role in Earth's history. Rivers and glaciers helped shape the planet's surface into what we see today. The first civilizations developed along rivers, too. Over time, communities began finding new ways to meet their water needs, including practicing irrigation and building **aqueducts**.

312 BC

Construction begins on the first Roman aqueduct. Over the next few centuries, Romans build several aqueduct systems designed to bring fresh water into cities.

1972 AD

The U.S. Congress passes the Clean Water Act. This law includes many regulations designed to reduce water pollution in the United States.

2019

The World Health Organization (WHO) reports that 2.2 billion people do not have access to safe drinking water. About 4.2 billion people lack safely managed sanitation services.

The Hydrosphere and the Atmosphere

The atmosphere is made up of layers of gases. It extends from the planet's surface up into space. Part of the water cycle involves water's interaction with the atmosphere. When water evaporates into the atmosphere, it is moved around by air currents. These air currents often carry the water vapor above oceans to land, increasing the supply of fresh water. Without air currents, the water cycle would not be possible.

Clouds exist because of the interaction between the hydrosphere and the atmosphere.

The ocean and the atmosphere also interact to move water and energy around Earth. Surface winds help to propel ocean currents. These currents carry warm water from the equator to the north and south poles. The Gulf Stream is one such current. It starts near the equator, travels up the east coast of the United States, then crosses the Atlantic Ocean and moves toward Europe. The relationship between air and water temperatures keeps both the hydrosphere and the atmosphere cycling around Earth.

Ocean currents can **move as quickly** as **5 miles per hour** (8 km/h).

The **Gulf Stream** has an **average speed** of **4 miles per hour** (6.4 km/h).

The **first chart** of the **Gulf Stream** was published by **Benjamin Franklin** in the **late 1700s**.

The Hydrosphere and the Biosphere

Many of Earth's animals are aquatic, which means they live in the hydrosphere.

The biosphere is made up of all living things, and water is essential for life on Earth. Plants and animals around the world have developed adaptations that help them use the water that is available in their environment.

Plants need water in order to take in **nutrients** from soil. The nutrients dissolve into water and are absorbed along with it by a plant's roots. Water also helps plants stand straight. Without water, plants wilt.

Cacti often grow in hot and dry areas such as deserts.

Certain plants have adaptations that allow them to live in places with little water. Cactus plants use their roots to collect as much water as possible. Some cacti have roots that grow close to the surface and spread over a large area to capture more water. Cacti may also have roots that grow deep into the ground in search of groundwater.

Most animals need fresh water to survive. The salt in salt water causes animals to become **dehydrated**. Ocean fish have adaptations that allow them to filter the salt out of the water they drink. Many marine mammals do not drink salt water. Instead, they get their water from the food they eat.

The **roots** of a **mesquite tree** can be **up to 80 feet** (24 meters) long.

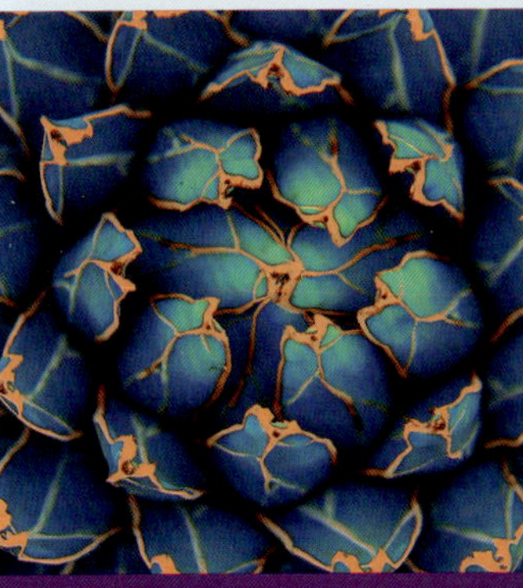

There are more than **2,000 cactus species**.

The ocean is home to **20,000 species** of **fish**.

The Hydrosphere and the Lithosphere

Over time, glacial movement can carve valleys and mountains.

The lithosphere is made up of all of the rocks and minerals on Earth. It provides a home for the hydrosphere by surrounding and supporting different bodies of water. In turn, the hydrosphere helps shape the lithosphere's surface through **weathering** and erosion. The hydrosphere also moves **sediment** from one part of the lithosphere to another.

During the last Ice Age, much of North America was covered by glaciers. The weight of the ice and snow piling up caused the bottom of the glaciers to slide forward. As the glaciers slid forward, they scraped the ground and pushed piles of rock and dirt ahead of them. When the glaciers **receded**, they left these piles, called moraines, behind. Moraines can be found today in places such as Moraine State Park in Pennsylvania. Glaciers also move large boulders and deposit them far from where they were picked up. These boulders are called **glacial erratics**.

Turquoise lakes get their brilliant blue-green color from sunlight reflecting off glacial silt.

As glaciers grow and recede, they grind rocks against each other. The rocks are worn down into a fine powder called glacial silt or rock flour. It contains important minerals that help plants grow. The silt gets washed into lakes and rivers by glacial melt and is gradually deposited into the soil along the way. This process helps to redistribute minerals and sediments throughout the lithosphere.

Alaska is estimated to have about **100,000 glaciers**.

Kettle Moraine in Wisconsin is up to **300 feet** (91 m) **high**.

One of the **largest glacial erratics** weighs **18,188 tons** (16,500 metric tons).

Activity

Build an Erosion Model

This activity will demonstrate how plant roots and other organic matter help prevent water erosion. Collect the materials and follow the instructions.

Billions of tons (metric tons) of soil are lost every year to soil erosion, including water erosion.

BEFORE YOU START

Be creative! Sometimes, things go wrong. Experiments do not always work as planned. If there is a problem, use your imagination to solve it.

What You Need

What You Do

1. Mark and cut out a large rectangular hole from one side of each bottle.
2. Lay each bottle on its side with the opening facing up.
3. Fill the bottles with soil.
4. Cover the soil in one bottle with the sod.
5. Cover the soil in another bottle with the mulch.
6. Use the twine to hang a clear cup from the neck of each bottle. Place the bottles at the edge of a table or flat surface so that the clear cups are hanging down.
7. Tape over the bottom half of each bottle's neck opening.
8. Use the watering can to simulate rain over the soil in each bottle.
9. Record your observations of the water that runs through the soil and into each clear cup.

Questions

1. Which cup contains the clearest water? Why?
2. Which cup contains the dirtiest water? Why?
3. What role does organic matter play in preventing erosion?

Hydrosphere Quiz

1

When did construction begin on the first Roman aqueduct?

2

What is the natural movement of water through the hydrosphere called?

3

What is a tidewater glacier?

4

What are the stilt houses in Tai O called?

5

What do greenhouse gases do?

6

How are some communities collecting water from fog?

7

In 18,000 BC, how much of Earth was covered by glaciers?

8

Which system provides a home for the hydrosphere?

9

How many cactus species are there?

10

What are piles of rock and dirt left behind by glaciers called?

ANSWER KEY

1. 312 BC **2.** The water cycle **3.** A glacier that extends into the ocean **4.** Pang uks **5.** Trap heat **6.** By setting up mesh nets on hillsides to collect water droplets from the fog **7.** Approximately 32 percent **8.** Lithosphere **9.** More than 2,000 **10.** Moraines

Key Words

aqueducts: artificial channels for carrying water across a distance
condenses: changes from a gas to a liquid due to cooling
dehydrated: caused water to be lost from something
desalination: the process of removing salt from water
dynamic: constantly changing
erosion: the movement of sediment by wind, water, and other natural forces
evaporate: change from a liquid to a gas due to heating
fossil fuels: energy sources made from coal, wood, oil, or natural gas
glacial erratics: stones and rocks that have been transported a significant distance by a glacier
glaciers: huge masses of ice that move slowly over land
halophytic: adapted to grow in salty soil or salt water
mangrove forest: wetland ecosystem usually found along the coast of tropical oceans
nutrients: substances used by organisms for growth and development
precipitation: rain, snow, hail, or sleet that falls from the sky to the ground
receded: moved back from a previous position
sediment: solid material that is moved by wind, water, or glaciers and deposited in a new location
typhoons: tropical storms in the Northwest Pacific Ocean region
weathering: the breaking down of rock into sediment by natural forces

Index

LIGHTBOX

SUPPLEMENTARY RESOURCES

Click on the plus icon ⊕ found in the bottom left corner of each spread to open additional teacher resources.

- Download and print the book's quizzes and activities
- Access curriculum correlations
- Explore additional web applications that enhance the Lightbox experience

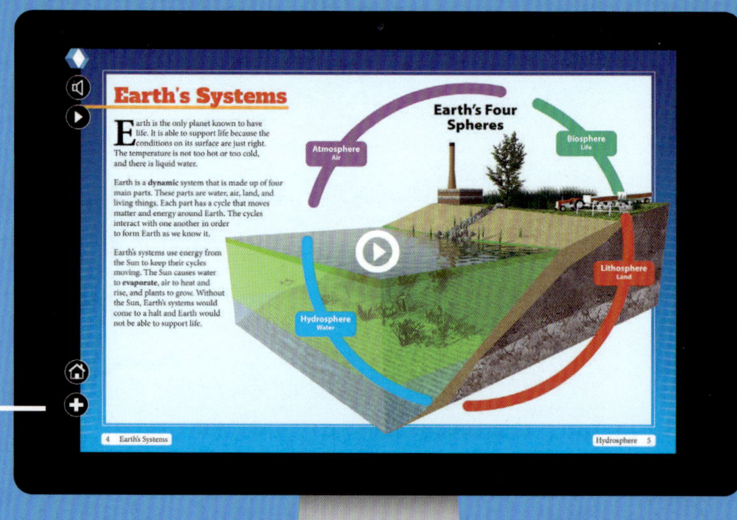

LIGHTBOX DIGITAL TITLES
Packed full of integrated media

VIDEOS

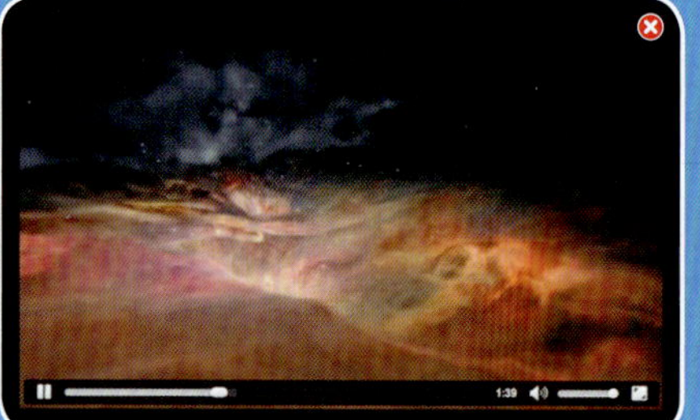

INTERACTIVE MAPS

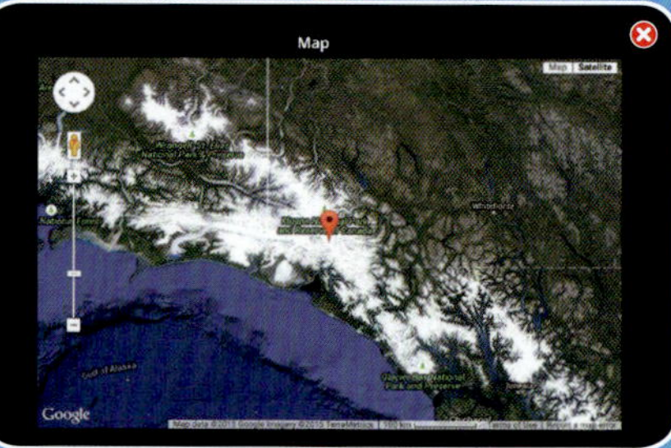

WEBLINKS

SLIDESHOWS

A cirque is a rounded, bowl-shaped area where snow collects.

QUIZZES

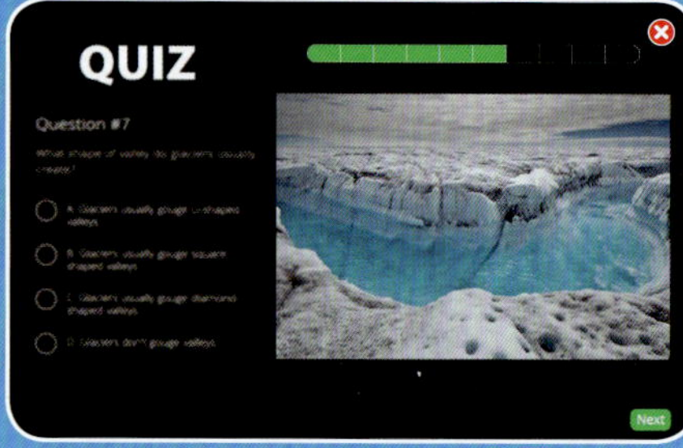

OPTIMIZED FOR

- ✓ TABLETS
- ✓ WHITEBOARDS
- ✓ COMPUTERS
- ✓ AND MUCH MORE!

Published by Smartbook Media Inc.
276 5th Avenue, Suite 704 #917
New York, NY 10001
Website: www.openlightbox.com

Library of Congress Cataloging-in-Publication Data

Names: Smith, Ryan, author.
Title: Hydrosphere / Ryan Smith.
Description: New York, NY : Smartbook Media Inc., [2022] | Series: Earth's systems | Includes index. | Audience: Ages: 10-12 | Audience: Grades: 4-6
Identifiers: LCCN 2021026096 (print) | LCCN 2021026097 (ebook) | ISBN 9781510553439 (library binding) | ISBN 9781510553446
Subjects: LCSH: Water--Juvenile literature. | Hydrology--Juvenile literature. | Hydrologic cycle--Juvenile literature.
Classification: LCC GB662.3 .S597 2022 (print) | LCC GB662.3 (ebook) | DDC 551.46--dc23
LC record available at https://lccn.loc.gov/2021026096
LC ebook record available at https://lccn.loc.gov/2021026097

Printed in Guangzhou, China
1 2 3 4 5 6 7 8 9 0 25 24 23 22 21

072021
111220

Project Coordinator: Priyanka Das
Art Director: Terry Paulhus

Photo Credits
Every reasonable effort has been made to trace ownership and to obtain permission to reprint copyright material. The publisher would be pleased to have any errors or omissions brought to its attention so that they may be corrected in subsequent printings. The publisher acknowledges Alamy and Getty Images as its primary image suppliers for this title.